SAINTS *a*

G000256667

Life in the Spirit
LINK-WORK BOOK

JOHN FINNEY AND
FELICITY LAWSON

helping you to help others

ISBN 1 84291 001 9

Published by
KINGSWAY PUBLICATIONS
Lottbridge Drove, Eastbourne BN23 6NT, England.
Email: books@kingsway.co.uk
in association with
Anglican Renewal Ministries
4 Bramble Street, Derby DE1 1HY
Email: saintsalive@anglican-renewal.org.uk

Cover design and print production for the publishers by
Bookprint Creative Services, P.O. Box 827, BN21 3YJ, England.
Printed in Great Britain.

Introduction

'I say to you: ask, and you will receive; seek, and you
will find; knock, and the door will be opened to you.
For all those who ask will receive, and those who seek
will find, and the door will be opened to anyone who
knocks.' *(Luke 11:9–10)*

▶ How to use this book

Welcome to the Saints Alive! *Life in the Spirit* course. Using
this link-work book regularly will help you to get the most out
of your group meetings and grow in your relationship with God.

You will also need a notebook. We recommend a spiral-bound
A5 size notebook because then it will match your Bible and
this link-work book, but any size would do. You can use your
notebook to:

- write down any thoughts or questions you have following
  your group meeting, things which you particularly want to
  remember or things you want to think about further;
- note down anything which strikes you as you do the chunk
  reading;
- reflect on the questions in the daily reading;
- keep a record of anything which you think God is
  particularly saying to you during the course.

What you write in your notebook is strictly personal and
private. You might find it helpful to take it to group meetings,
but no one will ask to see it.

This book contains two types of Bible reading: chunk readings
and daily readings.

 Chunk readings

The Bible was not written to be read only a few verses at a time, as we do in church. The chunk readings are designed to help you read the Bible the same way you might read a book – several chapters at a time. This way you get a better understanding of the whole story. Many people find this one of the most exciting and worthwhile parts of the course. During this course you will be encouraged to read the Gospel of Mark and the Acts of the Apostles. By doing this, you will have read about the life and ministry of Jesus and the story of the first Christians. Towards the end of the course you will be introduced to other ways of reading the Bible as well.

You may find it helpful to plan ahead and set aside about three-quarters of an hour each week when you can get comfortable and settle down to do your chunk reading. If you have poor eyesight or find reading difficult, ask your course leaders if they have a tape available so that you can listen to the chunk readings instead.

Daily readings

Many Christians find it helpful to try to read the Bible and pray every day. The daily readings are designed to help you do this. They supplement the teaching given during the course and are usually based on the previous week's session.

Try to set aside 10–15 minutes every day to be quiet and draw close to God. Choose a time of day when you are not too tired and won't be interrupted. Try to find a place where you can be by yourself and can relax. If you can't always manage every day, don't be disheartened. Some people find it easier than others to find the time and get into a routine. For instance, parents of young children or those who work shifts might find it especially difficult to establish a regular pattern. You can always catch up and do several days together if need be. But if you can get into a routine of daily prayer and Bible reading it will help you in the future, once the Saints Alive! course is ended.

Prayer

Prayer is simply being with God and sharing ourselves with him. There is no 'correct' way to pray, but if prayer is new to you, the following comments may be helpful.

When you pray:

- Be natural with God. Tell him what you really feel, in your own words, not just what you think he wants to hear. God loves us to share ourselves with him, and our first stumbling words of prayer are as precious to him as the first words of a baby are to its parents.

- There is no need to get into a special position to pray. Some people find it helpful to kneel, but you can sit, walk or lie down. It is important to be comfortable so that your attention can be focused on God and not on yourself.

- There are many different ways of praying:

   Praise: telling God how great he is and that you love him.

   Confession: when you know that you are in the wrong and that there has been a cloud between you and God – telling him you are sorry and asking for help to change.

   Thanksgiving: thanking God for what he has done for you and for others.

   Intercession: asking him for those things which you and others need. Try to keep a balance between praying for yourself and praying for other people.

   Silence: simply being quiet before God and soaking up his presence – rather like spiritual sunbathing.

- While it is important to have special times for prayer, we can talk to God at any time or place – at work, in the shops, even while having a bath. The more you pray, the more natural prayer will become.

● Let God speak to you through the Bible. St Augustine described the Bible as 'our letters from home'. Before you begin, ask God to help you to understand what you are reading and to hear his special message in it for you. Some of the readings in this booklet have questions for you to answer. These are to help you to understand what you are reading and to see how God's word fits your situation. This is for your use only – no one will ask to see your answers. It is important to use a modern version of the Bible. (The daily readings are based on the *Good News Bible*. If you have another version, you may sometimes find that different words are used from those in the questions.)

If at any time you are worried about prayer or Bible reading, or have questions about things which have been said during the course, please don't hesitate to ask one of your course leaders.

God will also speak to you through other members of the course. Make a note of their names in your notebook and begin to pray for them. Rejoice when the light and love of God is seen in their lives.

▶ A mini-guide to finding your way round the Bible

The Bible is divided into two parts: the Old Testament and the New Testament. Each part is divided into different books. The books in the Old Testament come from the time before Jesus while those in the New Testament describe his life and that of the early church. Each book is divided into chapters and verses.

Finding a particular reading

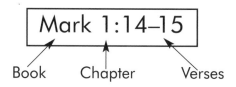

Every Bible has a contents page somewhere near the front which lists all the books in order. If you are new to the Bible, it will help you find books more quickly. (Some books have a number before them, e.g. 1 John or 2 Peter, because there is more than one book of the same name. Be sure you get the right one!) Most of the readings in this link-work book come from the New Testament, and we tell you when they come from the Old Testament.

Jesus said, 'I have come in order that you might have life – life in all its fullness.'

(John 10:10)

Chunk reading

The first four books in the New Testament are known as Gospels – Matthew, Mark, Luke and John. They all tell the story of the life and ministry and teaching of Jesus. They are not biographies or histories as we understand them – they don't pretend to tell us everything there is to know about him, though research has shown that they are historically reliable. They were written to help pass on the story of Jesus so that the first Christians could be strengthened and grow in their faith, and so that enquirers could discover for themselves who Jesus was and what he taught.

Matthew, Mark and Luke have much material in common with one another. John's approach and style of writing is rather different. Mark is the shortest of the Gospels and many people think it was the first to be written. We have chosen to begin our chunk reading with Mark. Some of the daily readings will help you to dip into the other Gospels.

➔ Read through Mark chapters 1–8. Try to read it through in one sitting and have two questions in your mind as you do so:
- What sort of person was Jesus?
- What kind of things did he do?

 # Daily readings

The Bible tells us that God loves each one of us and that he wants us to know him and trust him as Father. Jesus came to show us what God is like and to make it possible for us to know him and experience his love. Read what John wrote about Jesus in John 1:10–18. (In this passage 'the Word' is another name for Jesus.)

Spend a few minutes thanking God for his love and asking that you may come to know him better and to understand his plans for your life.

Psalm 23 in the Old Testament tells us of one person's experience of God. It may have been written by David who was a shepherd before he became king of Israel. It speaks about God's provision, guidance and protection. Are there ways in which this psalm speaks to you? You might like to make a note of any ideas which are especially important to you.

God made us to live in harmony with himself and to experience his love. However, for many people God seems far away. Isaiah 59:1–2 in the Old Testament explains what has gone wrong. Sin separates us from God. Sin is not only the wrong things which we do, it is also the attitude of independence which says that we can manage without God. In Romans 3:22–23 Paul tells us that everyone has sinned but that God restores our relationship with him through faith in Jesus Christ. Ask God to forgive you and draw you closer to himself through Jesus.

In the Old Testament God promises his people that a time will come when he will take the initiative to deal with sin. One place where you can read this promise is Ezekiel 36:25–28. The prophet Ezekiel uses picture language to help us understand spiritual truth. Make a note of the three things which God promises in this passage. The promises were fulfilled in Jesus who, through his death on the cross, has dealt with sin and made it possible for us to know God intimately.

 What do John 14:6 and 1 Timothy 2:5 tell us about Jesus?

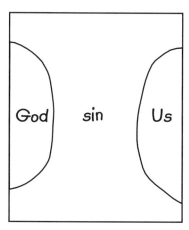

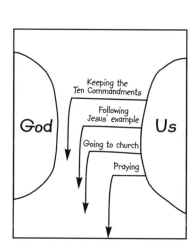

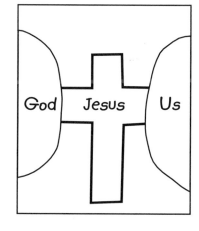

This diagram may have been used in last week's session.

Jesus often told stories (parables) to teach people about God. In Luke 15:11–32 he tells a story about a father and his son. What do you think Jesus wants us to learn from this story?

 Psalm 63:1–8 in the Old Testament speaks of one person's longing for God. Perhaps you could write a prayer or psalm expressing something of your longing for God?

Pray today for the group meeting and for all who will be there, that everyone will grow in their understanding of who Jesus is and what he has done for us.

2

'God showed his love for us by sending his only Son into the world, so that we might have life through him. This is what love is: it is not that we have loved God, but that he loved us and sent his Son to be the means by which our sins are forgiven.'

(1 John 4:9–10)

Chunk reading

→ Read through the rest of Mark's Gospel – chapters 9–16. Let two thoughts be in your mind:

- The people who crucified Jesus were not terrible people but ordinary people who, out of fear and self-concern, destroyed the only perfect, innocent human being who has ever lived.
- How much Jesus must love us to go through that for us.

Daily readings

DAY 1

Writing many centuries before Christ, the prophet Isaiah in the Old Testament foretold that the chosen servant of God would suffer for the sins of his people. Isaiah 52:13–15 and 53:1–12 is a long passage but it contains many remarkable parallels with what actually happened to Jesus. As you think about the crucifixion of Jesus, can you think of any?

Read Isaiah 52:13–15 and 53:1–12, the same passage from the Old Testament as yesterday. What answers does Isaiah give to the questions:

● Why did Jesus die?

● What was the result of his death?

 The first Christians quickly came to recognise that Jesus was more than just a good man. Read Colossians 1:15–22. Here Paul is writing some years after the crucifixion about the full grandeur of Christ. What does this passage tell us about:

● Who Jesus is?

● What he has achieved for us?

 On the Day of Pentecost Peter spoke to the crowds about Jesus. Read Acts 2:22–24 and 36–39. What did Peter say to them about Jesus? What did he tell them to do in order to receive God's promise of forgiveness and the Holy Spirit?

 Revelation 3:20 gives us a simple picture of how Jesus is waiting for us to ask him right into the centre of our lives. These words were originally addressed to Christians whose love for Jesus had grown cold, but they are equally applicable to people who have never before asked him to be Lord of their lives. What promise does Jesus give to those who open the door?

These four circles were used at the end of last week's session.

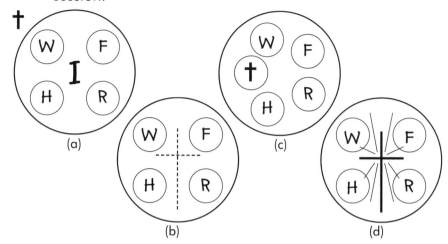

(a) For some people it is as if Jesus is right outside their lives.
(b) For some, knowledge and experience of Jesus is a faint memory.
(c) For some, Jesus is important but is in a 'compartment'.
(d) Jesus died that he might be Lord of every part of out lives.

 Read Mark 8:31–38. The first disciples found it hard to understand that Jesus' death and resurrection were all part of God's plan. Jesus goes on to say some things which we find hard to understand. What is the main point of verses 34–38?

 In John 6:35–40 Jesus makes three promises to those who come to him. What are they?

Pray especially today for your next session and ask that everyone may grow in their understanding of the resurrection of Jesus.

'Let us give thanks to the God and Father of our Lord Jesus Christ! Because of his great mercy he gave us new life by raising Jesus Christ from death.' *(1 Peter 1:3)*

Chunk reading

For the rest of the course we shall be reading the Acts of the Apostles.

Acts was written by Luke as a follow-up to his Gospel. You can see references to this in the first few verses of chapter 1. Acts is the story of the early church and shows how the good news of Jesus spread from Jerusalem to the Gentile world and eventually to Rome. The book has been called the 'Acts of the Holy Spirit' because the account of the coming of the Holy Spirit on the Day of Pentecost is the springboard for the rest of the book and Luke emphasises the work of the Holy Spirit throughout. Luke was a companion of Paul and experienced first-hand some of the events he writes about. (You can tell which bits these were because he begins to speak of 'we' instead of 'they'.)

➔ Read Acts chapters 1–5. As you do so notice:

- The references to the work of the Holy Spirit among the disciples.

- The part that various miraculous happenings played in the everyday life of the church. Such things were obviously regarded as fairly normal, just as they had been in the ministry of Jesus.

 **Daily readings**

Today you have another chance to look at part of the passage you studied in the last group meeting. Read Luke 24:1–35 and make a note of what strikes you as really important.

Not everyone found it easy to believe that Jesus really had been raised from the dead. In fact most of the disciples found it difficult even when their close friends said that they had seen him. You can read about one of them in John 20:24–31. What does Jesus say to Thomas which is important for us today?

In 1 Corinthians 15:1–7 Paul reminds the Christians at Corinth of three things which he says are of the greatest importance. Discover what these are and then give thanks for them.

The resurrection of Jesus gives us confidence that death has been conquered and that we too will rise to a new life in Christ. The Bible does not encourage us to look for precise details but in 1 Corinthians 15:35–38 and 42–50 Paul uses the picture of a seed to try and help his readers understand what will happen to us when we die. Adam is the name given to the first human being in the account of the creation given in the book of Genesis at the beginning of the Bible. Paul speaks about Jesus as 'the second Adam', the person who fulfilled all that human beings were intended to be.

Because Jesus has been raised from the dead we can experience something of his resurrection life here and now. Sin need no longer have the power over us which it once did. God requires our co-operation if we are to be changed to become more like Jesus in this life. In Colossians 3:1–14 Paul uses the idea of taking off one set of clothes and putting on another to show the difference between the old life and the new. Are there particular things in your life which you would like to 'take off' by the help of God?

Becoming more like Jesus does not happen overnight, though some people do experience a remarkable change when they become Christians. The only reason Paul writes in this way is because his readers are not yet perfect! The important thing is to want to change and to seek God's help in doing so.

You could use the following prayer: 'Lord, please change the world and begin with me.'

Each of the Gospels records that the risen Jesus, before he left his disciples, gave them a special commission. In last week's session the group looked together at Luke 24:45–53. Look today at Matthew 28:16–20. What are Jesus' parting instructions and promises? (You might like to compare Matthew's version and Luke's version.)

Jesus did not expect the disciples to go 'into all the world and preach the gospel' unaided. He provided them with a Helper (the Holy Spirit). Read John 14:25–26 and John 15:26–27. What do these verses teach us about the Helper?

In the group meeting today we shall be thinking about the work of the Holy Spirit in the individual and the church. Some of the ideas may be new to you and other members of the group. Pray that the Holy Spirit will give you understanding and a desire to experience more of his power in your lives.

'When the Holy Spirit comes upon you, you will be filled with power, and you will be witnesses for me in Jerusalem, in all Judaea and Samaria, and to the ends of the earth.' *(Acts 1:8)*

Chunk reading

→ Read Acts chapters 6–11. (You might like to miss out 7:1–50 which is heavy going if you don't know much Old Testament history.) The church began in Jerusalem but, following the persecution that began with the death of Stephen, Christians were scattered throughout the region and to other places where there were Jews. Wherever they went they spoke of their faith in Jesus. In chapter 9 we read of the conversion of Saul of Tarsus (later known as Paul), one of the most influential Christian missionaries, teachers and leaders of all time. It was Paul who wrote many of the letters which are preserved in the New Testament. In chapters 10 and 11 we read of the conversion of Cornelius and his household. Although he was a God-fearer (someone who worshipped at the Jewish synagogue), he was a Gentile. As you will see from the story, Jews and Gentiles did not normally mix, so here we have a marvellous example of the good news of Jesus leaping over racial and cultural barriers.

Daily readings

Just as Jesus had promised, the Holy Spirit was poured out on the first disciples on the Day of Pentecost, transforming them from a bunch of frightened men and women to bold and courageous witnesses. As we read the Acts of the Apostles, we see that same Holy Spirit continuing to fill people's lives, sometimes for the first time, sometimes filling them afresh. The first few days this week draw your attention to particular passages which you will also be reading as part of your chunk reading. As you read them, remember that the Holy Spirit still comes to people in the same way today.

Read Acts 4:23–31. As the first Christians gather together for prayer following the arrest of Peter and John, they are filled afresh with the Holy Spirit and go out boldly for Christ. Notice how they begin their prayer by praising God for who he is, asserting his greatness in the face of the threats against them. What do they ask God for? How can our prayers be equally trusting and bold?

In accordance with the prophecy of Acts 1:8, the gospel had spread into the area of Samaria through the preaching of Philip, and there was 'great joy in the city'(Acts 8:8). On this occasion the new believers received the Holy Spirit through the laying on of hands. Read Acts 8:4–8,14–17. How were Philip and Peter and John able to tell that 'the Holy Spirit had not yet come down on any of them'?

In Acts 9:1–19 we read of the dramatic encounter between Christ and Saul on the Damascus road. Ananias played an important part in the story. Imagine how he must have felt when God asked him to go and see Paul. Are there things we can learn from this story?

 In Acts 10:34–48 Peter has gone to visit Cornelius. God takes the initiative and takes Peter by surprise. Notice that on this occasion the Holy Spirit was given before Cornelius had had a chance to respond to Peter's preaching or to be baptised. We must be careful not to try to programme the way in which God will work in people's lives.

 When the Holy Spirit came upon the disciples at Pentecost, he created a new kind of community – the Christian church – which is beautifully described in Acts 2:41–47. What were the distinctive features of that community?

 In Acts 13:1–5 the Holy Spirit sends Paul and Barnabas to do missionary work in Cyprus and beyond. What were the five men doing when the Spirit spoke to them? How could this way of doing things fit in the church today?

 In Romans 8 Paul teaches about the work of the Holy Spirit in the life of a Christian. It may be helpful to write a list of the things mentioned in verses 14–17 and 26–27.

Pray for the group meeting today, that everyone will grow in their understanding of the work of the Holy Spirit in our lives.

5

'The Spirit's presence is shown in some way in each person for the good of all.' *(1 Corinthians 12:7)*

Chunk reading

→ Read Acts chapters 12–15. Chapters 13 and 14 tell of Paul's first missionary journey. In chapter 15 we read of a major disagreement between the Jewish Christians and Paul and his friends from Antioch about whether Gentile Christians had to obey Jewish religious laws. The argument may be hard for us to understand but a very important principle was at stake – the basis on which people become Christians (15:9–11). There is nothing necessarily wrong in Christians disagreeing with one another, providing both sides are prepared for God to teach them something new and to bring truth out of their discussions in the way that he did in Acts 15.

Daily readings

In the last session we thought about the gifts of the Spirit mentioned by Paul in 1 Corinthians 12 and how they are rather like a Christian's tool kit. 1 Peter 4:10–11 also refers to the gifts of the Spirit and, rather than being specific, groups them in two categories of preaching and serving. Notice that Peter, just like Paul, says that every Christian is given gifts. What can be learnt from this passage about why they are given and how they are to be used?

Paul often contrasts the character of unbridled human nature with life in the Spirit. One place where he does this is Galatians 5:16–26. Are there any particular 'fruits of the Spirit' which you would like to see more of in your life?

 The story of Zacchaeus in Luke 19:1–10 gives us a practical example of what it means to come to Christ and repent (say sorry for the past and change direction). Next week you will have an opportunity to commit your life to Christ and pray for the power of the Holy Spirit in your life. As part of that you will have an opportunity to make the baptismal promises:

I repent of my sins

I renounce evil

I turn to Christ

Is there anything in particular for which you want to ask God's forgiveness?

 To have faith is to put our trust not in our ability to help ourselves but in what Jesus has done for us by his death and resurrection. The familiar verses in John 3:16–17 remind us of this. If you have come to a point of believing in Jesus, try rewriting verse 16 putting your own name in place of the word 'everyone'. Thank God for the gift of eternal life in Jesus.

 The most common thing which stops us from moving forward with Christ is fear. Some people are afraid of what other people will think of them. Others are afraid of letting God really take control of their lives. Still others are afraid that their sins and weaknesses are so great that God cannot possibly help them. In 2 Timothy 1:7 fear is described as 'timidity'. Note the positive qualities the Holy Spirit gives us.

 In Luke 11:9–13 Jesus assures his disciples that the Holy Spirit is a good gift and that he will be given to all who ask. What reason does Jesus give for this assurance?

 In John 7:37–39 Jesus gives a promise to all who are thirsty. He describes the Holy Spirit as 'streams of life-giving water'. What do we have to do in order to experience the Holy Spirit in this way?

Pray for the group meeting today, that everyone will be filled to overflowing with the love and power of God the Holy Spirit.

WEEK

6

'Let us give thanks to the God and Father of our Lord Jesus Christ! For in our union with Christ he has blessed us by giving us every spiritual blessing in the heavenly world.' *(Ephesians 1:3)*

Chunk reading

→ Chapters 16–20 of Acts record Paul's second and third missionary journeys and tell of how, despite fierce opposition, the good news of Jesus reaches through Turkey to Greece. What was it that motivated Paul and his companions in the face of so many difficulties?

Daily readings

DAY 1

Titus 3:4–7 reminds us of the heart of the Christian good news. God's gift of new life through Jesus in the power of the Holy Spirit is for all who truly turn to him. Some people have wonderful spiritual experiences when they surrender their lives to God. Other people do not experience anything very much at all. Scripture reminds us that God's character and what he has done for us in Christ are the basis of our faith and not any feelings we might or might not have. Whether or not you felt God touch you in a special way at the last group meeting, praise him for his free gift of new life in Christ. Pray for all who received prayer at the last group meeting, that they may know that God is with them. If you did not receive prayer yourself, it may be appropriate later. If necessary, talk it through with your group leader.

 Psalm 145 in the Old Testament is a song of praise for who God is and what he has done. In verse 13 it reminds us that 'the Lord is faithful to his promises'. If you have just committed or recommitted your life to Christ, he promises, 'I will never leave you; I will never abandon you' (Hebrews 13:5).

Perhaps you would like to write your own song of praise to God? (Don't worry about putting it in verses or trying to make it rhyme!)

 In Ephesians 1 Paul invites his readers to 'give thanks to God ... [and] praise his glory'. He records all that God has done in Christ. Read verses 3–8 and 13–14 and make a list of what he has done for you.

Now praise him for what he has done and pray that the truth of these verses may become increasingly part of your Christian experience.

 In Ephesians 1:15–23 Paul prays for his readers that they may grow in their faith. Why not pray verses 17–19 for the other members of your group?

 Proverbs 3:5–8 in the Old Testament gives some wise advice for those who wish to follow God's plans for their lives. Does any part of this strike you as particularly important?

When the Holy Spirit of truth is invited into any part of our lives, one of the first things he often does is to show up the dark places. 1 John 1:5 – 2:2 reminds us what to do when we are aware of sin in our lives. It is helpful to write down the promises God gives us in 1:9 and 2:2.

 If you have been doing your chunk reading in Acts, you will realise that being a Christian is no guarantee of an easy life. James 1:2–8 says that we ought to think ourselves fortunate when problems arise because they give us the opportunity to strengthen our faith. Are there any difficulties which you have met recently that have strengthened your faith?

7

'I am the vine, and you are the branches. Those who remain in me, and I in them, will bear much fruit; for you can do nothing without me.' *(John 15:5)*

Chunk reading

→ This week the story of the early church as recorded in the Acts of the Apostles reaches its climax as Paul finally reaches Rome, at that time the centre of the known world. Chapters 21–28 tell of Paul's courage as he faces both legal trials and physical danger, confident that God's ultimate purposes cannot be thwarted by human beings.

Daily readings

DAY 1 If we are to grow in Christ then there needs to be a degree of determination and persistence. What does Colossians 2:6–7 say we should do to become mature Christians?

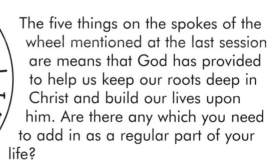

The five things on the spokes of the wheel mentioned at the last session are means that God has provided to help us keep our roots deep in Christ and build our lives upon him. Are there any which you need to add in as a regular part of your life?

In Luke 6:46–49 Jesus told a story about the importance of laying strong foundations for our lives. How does he say this can be done?

 Ephesians 6:10–18 describes the Christian life as a spiritual battle. Make a list of the armour which God gives us. It can be helpful to consciously put on the armour of Christ, especially when we are being tempted or facing particular troubles or difficulties.

 One of the spokes of the wheel in last week's session was the Bible. In 2 Timothy 3:14–17 Paul writes to Timothy of the importance of studying the Scriptures. What does he say they are useful for?

There are many ways of reading and studying Scripture other than those used on this course. Your leaders will have suggestions of books and booklets that will be able to help you continue to grow in your understanding of the Bible and enable you to feed on God's word which comes to you through its pages. It is important that we study the Scriptures with others as well as on our own. You can talk with your leaders about ways in which this happens in your church.

 We conclude our daily readings on the Saints Alive! *Life in the Spirit* course by reading Romans 12 in three sections. This chapter has been described as 'guidelines for living the Christian life'.

Offering ourselves to Christ is not a once-for-all decision – it needs to be renewed daily. Think carefully through the verses of Romans 12:1–2 and determine to offer your life afresh to God at the beginning of each new day. When we do this God promises that we will know his will.

J. B. Phillips translated 'Do not conform yourselves to the standards of this world' as 'Do not allow the world to squeeze you into its mould'. You might find it helpful to jot down some of the pressures which you feel might fit this description.

When we become a Christian we become part of God's family, the church. Paul often uses the idea of the church as a body to remind his readers that Christians are given different gifts and need each other. How does he describe this in Romans 12:3–8?

In the last part of Romans 12 Paul talks about the attitudes and actions which should characterise the Christian family. Read verses 9–21. Make a list of what he considers to be important and ask God to help you with things which you might find particularly difficult.

Pray for your group meeting today as you think together about what it means to be part of the church.

I ....

have decided before Christ that I will seek his help to be a loyal member of

.... **Church.**

As a loyal member, I will:

◆ be regular in worship and prepare for it with care

◆ join with others for fellowship, prayer and study

◆ give care and practical help to those within and outside the church, especially those in greatest need

◆ give regular financial support

◆ exercise the gifts God has given to me

◆ pray for members of the church

◆ accept and support the leadership – not unthinkingly, but as a responsible adult

◆ continue to think about my faith and how it relates to my home, work, recreation and the other parts of my life

◆ seek to share my faith with others (by praying for them, looking for opportunities to talk to them and inviting them into the fellowship).

Signed ....   **Date** ....